GW00320326

BUILDINGS IN THE LANDSCAPE
Ireland Yearbook 2005

A Collection of Irish Paintings from the Ulster Museum

First published by Appletree Press Ltd, 14 Howard Street South, Belfast BT7 1AP

Copyright © Appletree Press 2003. Text © Appletree Press 2003.

Photographs reproduced with the kind permission of the Trustees of the National Museums and Galleries of Northern Ireland.

All rights reserved. No part of this publication may be reproduced or transmitted in any form or by any means, electronic or mechanical, photocopying, recording or in any information or retrieval system without prior permission in writing from the publisher.

BUILDINGS IN THE LANDSCAPE
Ireland Yearbook 2005

A Collection of Irish Paintings from the Ulster Museum

Foreword

This inspiring selection of paintings on the theme of buildings and their place in the Irish landscape has been drawn from the Ulster Museum's Fine Art Collections. The Collections – paintings, sculpture, drawings, watercolours and prints – cover a wide spectrum of works, from the 16th century to the present day.

The Friends of the National Collections of Ireland and the Contemporary Art Society have for many years made generous gifts to the Museum. The help of such grant-awarding bodies as The National Art Collections Fund, National Heritage Memorial Fund, the Heritage Lottery Fund and the Esmé Mitchell Trust has been instrumental in enabling the Museum to further enhance its Applied Art holdings. These include significant collections of historic Irish glass and silver, alongside furniture, costume, textiles and jewellery.

The Museum's historical collection of British and Irish watercolours includes extensive holdings by the 19th-century Belfast artists Andrew Nicholl (1804–86) and Dr James Moore (1819–83).

With collections spanning Irish, British, continental European and North American items, the Museum has the most comprehensive assembly of 20th-century art in Ireland.

The Ulster Museum is part of the National Museums and Galleries of Northern Ireland.

Achill Island, Co. Mayo

1913

Robert Henri *(1863-1929)*

Oil on board
32.2 x 40.5 cm

December 2004

M		6	13	20	27
T		7	14	21	28
W	1	8	15	22	29
T	2	9	16	23	30
F	3	10	17	24	31
S	4	11	18	25	
S	5	12	19	26	

January 2005

M		3	10	17	24	31
T		4	11	18	25	
W		5	12	19	26	
T		6	13	20	27	
F		7	14	21	28	
S	1	8	15	22	29	
S	2	9	16	23	30	

February 2005

M		7	14	21	28
T	1	8	15	22	
W	2	9	16	23	
T	3	10	17	24	
F	4	11	18	25	
S	5	12	19	26	
S	6	13	20	27	

One of the leading painters of the American Impressionist movement, Robert Henri was born Robert Henry Cozad, son of a professional gambler. When he was eighteen his father shot dead another man in a gambling argument in the frontier town of Cozad, Nebraska, which he had founded. Though the killing was accepted as self-defence, the Cozad family fled east to avoid reprisals from the dead man's family. Some of them thought it wise to change their names. Robert adopted the French form of his middle name, but insisted in pronouncing it American style, "Hen-rye" (as in "buck eye"). After studying in Philadelphia and Paris, Henri came first to Achill Island in July 1913, the time when this little picture was painted. He formed many friendships and returned there in March 1924.

ROBERT HENRI

DECEMBER 2004

Week 1

December 2004					
M		6	13	20	27
T		7	14	21	28
W	1	8	15	22	29
T	2	9	16	23	30
F	3	10	17	24	31
S	4	11	18	25	
S	5	12	19	26	

MONDAY 27

Drove to London as Paddy (Joan's husband) had a stroke on Friday night. Joan is devastated. Arrived late afternoon. Took Tasa with us. Worried needlessly how she would re-act to Charlie (Joan's dog) but they got on well together.
Watched reports of the terrible tsunami in the Indian ocean yesterday.

TUESDAY 28

Visited Paddy in hospital in the morning. He has managed to say a few words but is still pretty ill. Joan and I took the bus to an Ealing Shopping Centre in the afternoon to stock up with food etc.
Talked over 'old times' in the evening.

WEDNESDAY 29

Looked in on Paddy for a few minutes then left Joan to stay with him for a few hours and went back to her house. There's not that much we can do to help except keep her company at night. Paddy making steady progress.

THURSDAY 30

Left London just after 9.00 am and arrived back in Jedburgh mid-afterno
Good journey up. Used our Sat-nav system.
Glad to be back home.
Had to come back as Sam's medication runs out tomorrow.

FRIDAY 31

Tasa is one year old today. Naomi (her breeder) sent an email birthday card. Took a photo and emailed it back to her.
Did the Cricket Field walk at Harestanes.
Went down with a terrible cold bug in the evening. Missed the New Ye

SATURDAY 1 / SUNDAY 2

Feeling pretty grotty today so spent most of it in bed.
Sam went down with the same bug in the evening.

Phoned Joan in the evening. Paddy making good progress.

January 2005

M		3	10	17	24	31
T		4	11	18	25	
W		5	12	19	26	
T		6	13	20	27	
F		7	14	21	28	
S	1	8	15	22	29	
S	2	9	16	23	30	

JANUARY 2005

Week 2

MONDAY 3

TUESDAY 4

WEDNESDAY 5

THURSDAY 6

FRIDAY 7

Snowdrops in bloom at
Gaveslanes
Severe flooding

SATURDAY 8 / SUNDAY 9

Small Farm, Donegal

Date unknown

Adam Tannochie Donald *(1911-1991)*

Pencil, watercolour on paper
26.7 x 36.8 cm

After attending school in the coastal village of Culross, Tann Donald studied at Edinburgh College of Art where he received his diploma. In the early 1930s he came to Northern Ireland to take up a post as Art Advisor to primary schools in Co. Londonderry. He returned to Ireland after war service to teach art at Limavady Technical College, but in the late 1940s moved to Belfast, where he taught life drawing and painting at the College of Art, and was known for the personal support he gave to individual students. In the early 1950s he was appointed Art Advisor to the Belfast Education Authority, remaining there for twenty years until his retirement.

December 2004

M		6	13	20	27
T		7	14	21	28
W	1	8	15	22	29
T	2	9	16	23	30
F	3	10	17	24	31
S	4	11	18	25	
S	5	12	19	26	

January 2005

M		3	10	17	24	31
T		4	11	18	25	
W		5	12	19	26	
T		6	13	20	27	
F		7	14	21	28	
S	1	8	15	22	29	
S	2	9	16	23	30	

February 2005

M		7	14	21	28
T	1	8	15	22	
W	2	9	16	23	
T	3	10	17	24	
F	4	11	18	25	
S	5	12	19	26	
S	6	13	20	27	

DONALD

JANUARY 2005

Week 3

January 2005

M		3	10	17	24	31
T		4	11	18	25	
W		5	12	19	26	
T		6	13	20	27	
F		7	14	21	28	
S	1	8	15	22	29	
S	2	9	16	23	30	

MONDAY 10

TUESDAY 11

WEDNESDAY 12

THURSDAY 13

FRIDAY 14

Kerstin Ian Daniel and adam arrived for the weekend.

SATURDAY 15 / SUNDAY 16

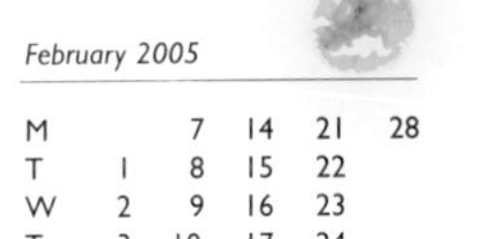

February 2005

M		7	14	21	28
T	1	8	15	22	
W	2	9	16	23	
T	3	10	17	24	
F	4	11	18	25	
S	5	12	19	26	
S	6	13	20	27	

JANUARY 2005

Week 4

MONDAY 17

Blossom on the two cherry trees in the back garden.

Slight fall of snow.

TUESDAY 18

WEDNESDAY 19

THURSDAY 20

FRIDAY 21

SATURDAY 22 / SUNDAY 23

Londonderry Base

1944

Roland Vivian Pitchforth *(1895-1982)*

Pencil, watercolour on paper
46.8 x 77 cm

December 2004

M		6	13	20	27
T		7	14	21	28
W	1	8	15	22	29
T	2	9	16	23	30
F	3	10	17	24	31
S	4	11	18	25	
S	5	12	19	26	

January 2005

M		3	10	17	24	31
T		4	11	18	25	
W		5	12	19	26	
T		6	13	20	27	
F		7	14	21	28	
S	1	8	15	22	29	
S	2	9	16	23	30	

February 2005

M		7	14	21	28
T	1	8	15	22	
W	2	9	16	23	
T	3	10	17	24	
F	4	11	18	25	
S	5	12	19	26	
S	6	13	20	27	

Pitchforth studied at Wakefield School of Art 1912-14, Leeds College of Art 1914-15 and 1919-20, and at the Royal College of Art 1921-25 under William Rothenstein and Leon Underwood. His service in the Artillery during the First World War damaged his hearing, and he eventually became deaf. Between 1940 and 1945 he was an Official War Artist, first documenting urban bomb damage, and later attached to the Admiralty. He is regarded as one of the most versatile of the War Artists, and his experience in painting architecture served him well. This is an extensive view of Derry City from the Waterside, with the spires of St Eugene's Cathedral and the Guildhall, and a submarine in the River Foyle. As late as 1940 the British still hoped for access to their former naval base of Lough Swilly, Co. Donegal, which De Valera refused them. Londonderry was made the westernmost allied naval base in Europe, the furthest port from enemy bases, and was developed into an anti-U-boat training base.

JANUARY 2005

January 2005

M		3	10	17	24	31
T		4	11	18	25	
W		5	12	19	26	
T		6	13	20	27	
F		7	14	21	28	
S	1	8	15	22	29	
S	2	9	16	23	30	

Week 5

MONDAY 24

TUESDAY 25

WEDNESDAY 26

Crocus in bloom in front garden

THURSDAY 27

FRIDAY 28

Three clumps of primroses in bloom at the empty cottage near Bonjedward House

SATURDAY 29 / SUNDAY 30

JANUARY / FEBRUARY 2005

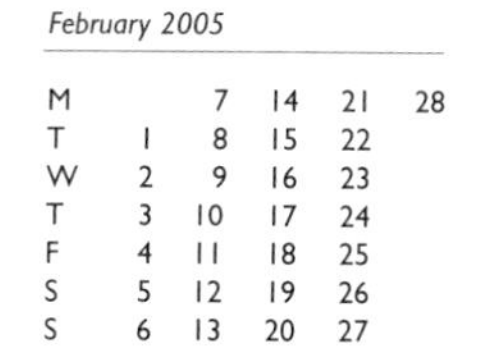
February 2005

M		7	14	21	28
T	1	8	15	22	
W	2	9	16	23	
T	3	10	17	24	
F	4	11	18	25	
S	5	12	19	26	
S	6	13	20	27	

Week 6

MONDAY 31

TUESDAY 1

WEDNESDAY 2

THURSDAY 3

FRIDAY 4

SATURDAY 5 / SUNDAY 6

View of the Cathedral and Mall, Downpatrick

1850

James Glen Wilson *(1827–1863)*

Oil on canvas
22.8 x 30.9 cm

January 2005

M		3	10	17	24	31
T		4	11	18	25	
W		5	12	19	26	
T		6	13	20	27	
F		7	14	21	28	
S	1	8	15	22	29	
S	2	9	16	23	30	

February 2005

M		7	14	21	28
T	1	8	15	22	
W	2	9	16	23	
T	3	10	17	24	
F	4	11	18	25	
S	5	12	19	26	
S	6	13	20	27	

March 2005

M		7	14	21	28
T	1	8	15	22	29
W	2	9	16	23	30
T	3	10	17	24	31
F	4	11	18	25	
S	5	12	19	26	
S	6	13	20	27	

The pleasing Georgian architecture of Downpatrick, with the distinctive cupola of the Southwell Charity almshouses of 1733 seen on the left of this painting, and the spiky, repetitive pinnacles of Down Cathedral at the culmination of English Street, are captured in evening sunlight in this charming painting. Little is known about the artist, other than that he joined the Navy in 1852 and that he produced several beautifully detailed marine paintings such as *Belfast Quay* (1851) and *Emigrant Ship Leaving Belfast* (1852) both also in the Ulster Museum – Belfast was therefore a frequent 'port of call' and the artist evidently also ventured into County Down to the reputed resting place of St Patrick. Wilson is known to have been appointed Surveyor by the New South Wales Department of Lands and in 1860 was transferred to Molong, 200 miles west of Sydney, where he died three years later.

FEBRUARY 2005

February 2005

M		7	14	21	28
T	1	8	15	22	
W	2	9	16	23	
T	3	10	17	24	
F	4	11	18	25	
S	5	12	19	26	
S	6	13	20	27	

Week 7

MONDAY 7

THURSDAY 10

TUESDAY 8

FRIDAY 11

WEDNESDAY 9

SATURDAY 12 / SUNDAY 13

March 2005

M		7	14	21	28
T	1	8	15	22	29
W	2	9	16	23	30
T	3	10	17	24	31
F	4	11	18	25	
S	5	12	19	26	
S	6	13	20	27	

FEBRUARY 2005

Week 8

MONDAY 14

THURSDAY 17

TUESDAY 15

FRIDAY 18

WEDNESDAY 16

SATURDAY 19 / SUNDAY 20

Her Little Holding

c. 1920

Hans Iten *(1874–1930)*

Oil on board
26.8 x 34.8 cm

January 2005

M		3	10	17	24	31
T		4	11	18	25	
W		5	12	19	26	
T		6	13	20	27	
F		7	14	21	28	
S	1	8	15	22	29	
S	2	9	16	23	30	

February 2005

M		7	14	21	28
T	1	8	15	22	
W	2	9	16	23	
T	3	10	17	24	
F	4	11	18	25	
S	5	12	19	26	
S	6	13	20	27	

March 2005

M		7	14	21	28
T	1	8	15	22	29
W	2	9	16	23	30
T	3	10	17	24	31
F	4	11	18	25	
S	5	12	19	26	
S	6	13	20	27	

Hans Iten, though Swiss, spent most of his working life in Belfast as a damask designer with the linen firm of McCrum, Watson and Mercer in Linenhall Street. One of the most accomplished painters in the city at the time, Iten was an active member of the Belfast Art Society. He exhibited widely – at the Paris Salon, the Glasgow Institute, the Royal Academy and the Royal Hibernian Academy. Iten maintained his continental links throughout his life, and died in Switzerland while convalescing after an operation. The Ulster Museum holds several of the artist's works. This charming depiction of a vernacular cottage overlooking the sea at Ardglass, Co. Down, was painted *en plein air* – Iten painted Ardglass many times and it was one of his favourite localities, where he knew many people. The Ulster Museum holds another Ardglass scene by Iten, *Surge of the Sea, Ardglass.*

FEBRUARY 2005

February 2005					
M		7	14	21	28
T	1	8	15	22	
W	2	9	16	23	
T	3	10	17	24	
F	4	11	18	25	
S	5	12	19	26	
S	6	13	20	27	

Week 9

MONDAY 21

TUESDAY 22

WEDNESDAY 23

THURSDAY 24

FRIDAY 25

SATURDAY 26 / SUNDAY 27

March 2005

M		7	14	21	28
T	1	8	15	22	29
W	2	9	16	23	30
T	3	10	17	24	31
F	4	11	18	25	
S	5	12	19	26	
S	6	13	20	27	

FEBRUARY / MARCH 2005

Week 10

MONDAY 28

TUESDAY 1

WEDNESDAY 2

THURSDAY 3

FRIDAY 4

SATURDAY 5 / SUNDAY 6

The Late William Dougherty's Fowl Stores

1869

Thomas Semple *(19th century)*

Oil on canvas
59.3 x 89 cm

This engaging primitive painting is dated 1869 and was donated by Miss M A McGowan in 1959. The detailing is interesting, particularly in the fascination with wheeled transport – carts or barrows. The chicken farm has an impressive triumphal arch as entry – indicating that William Dougherty wished to impress his customers.

February 2005

M		7	14	21	28
T	1	8	15	22	
W	2	9	16	23	
T	3	10	17	24	
F	4	11	18	25	
S	5	12	19	26	
S	6	13	20	27	

March 2005

M		7	14	21	28
T	1	8	15	22	29
W	2	9	16	23	30
T	3	10	17	24	31
F	4	11	18	25	
S	5	12	19	26	
S	6	13	20	27	

April 2005

M		4	11	18	25
T		5	12	19	26
W		6	13	20	27
T		7	14	21	28
F	1	8	15	22	29
S	2	9	16	23	30
S	3	10	17	24	

THE LATE. WILLIAM DOUGHERTY'S FOWL STORES.
T. Semple.

MARCH 2005

March 2005

M		7	14	21	28
T	1	8	15	22	29
W	2	9	16	23	30
T	3	10	17	24	31
F	4	11	18	25	
S	5	12	19	26	
S	6	13	20	27	

Week 11

MONDAY 7

TUESDAY 8

WEDNESDAY 9

THURSDAY 10

FRIDAY 11

SATURDAY 12 / SUNDAY 13

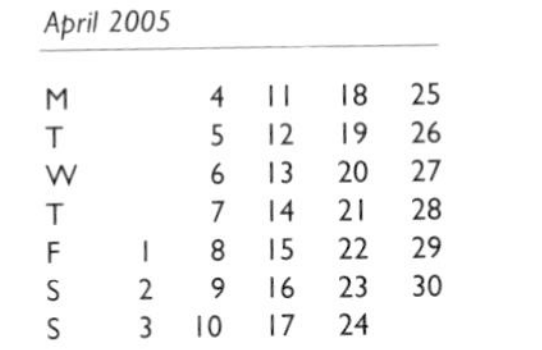

April 2005

M		4	11	18	25
T		5	12	19	26
W		6	13	20	27
T		7	14	21	28
F	1	8	15	22	29
S	2	9	16	23	30
S	3	10	17	24	

MARCH 2005

Week 12

MONDAY 14

TUESDAY 15

WEDNESDAY 16

THURSDAY 17

FRIDAY 18

SATURDAY 19 / SUNDAY 20

Dunluce Castle

1945

Eric Hesketh Hubbard *(1892–1957)*

Oil on canvas
64.1 x 76.6 cm

February 2005

M		7	14	21	28
T	1	8	15	22	
W	2	9	16	23	
T	3	10	17	24	
F	4	11	18	25	
S	5	12	19	26	
S	6	13	20	27	

March 2005

M		7	14	21	28
T	1	8	15	22	29
W	2	9	16	23	30
T	3	10	17	24	31
F	4	11	18	25	
S	5	12	19	26	
S	6	13	20	27	

April 2005

M		4	11	18	25
T		5	12	19	26
W		6	13	20	27
T		7	14	21	28
F	1	8	15	22	29
S	2	9	16	23	30
S	3	10	17	24	

This dramatic painting depicts the stark and impressive ruins of Dunluce Castle situated between Portballintrae and Portrush on the north Antrim coast. The stone towers and gables of the castle appear to rise out of the rocky outcrop – a bluff structure against the elements which have partly claimed it. The work was bought from the 1945 Annual Exhibition in Suffolk Street, London, of the Royal Society of British Artists, of which Hesketh Hubbard served as President from 1950 to 1956. Hubbard specialised in architectural painting, and visited Ireland frequently to paint and lecture. He studied at Heatherley's School of Art, Croyden School of Art and Chelsea Polytechnic, and lived for some time in Salisbury before moving back to London. He was a member of the Cheltenham Group of artists. Hubbard published a number of technical manuals on painting and printmaking, such as *First Principles of Oil Painting* which appeared as an artists' handbook in 1955.

HESKETH HUBBARD

MARCH 2005

March 2005

M		7	14	21	28
T	1	8	15	22	29
W	2	9	16	23	30
T	3	10	17	24	31
F	4	11	18	25	
S	5	12	19	26	
S	6	13	20	27	

Week 13

MONDAY 21

THURSDAY 24

TUESDAY 22

FRIDAY 25

WEDNESDAY 23

SATURDAY 26 / SUNDAY 27

MARCH / APRIL 2005

April 2005

M		4	11	18	25
T		5	12	19	26
W		6	13	20	27
T		7	14	21	28
F	1	8	15	22	29
S	2	9	16	23	30
S	3	10	17	24	

Week 14

MONDAY 28

THURSDAY 31

TUESDAY 29

FRIDAY 1

WEDNESDAY 30

SATURDAY 2 / SUNDAY 3

Ruin at Ardmore

c. 1946

Evie Hone *(1894–1955)*

Oil on panel
46.3 x 55.2 cm

March 2005

M		7	14	21	28
T	1	8	15	22	29
W	2	9	16	23	30
T	3	10	17	24	31
F	4	11	18	25	
S	5	12	19	26	
S	6	13	20	27	

April 2005

M		4	11	18	25
T		5	12	19	26
W		6	13	20	27
T		7	14	21	28
F	1	8	15	22	29
S	2	9	16	23	30
S	3	10	17	24	

May 2005

M		2	9	16	23	30
T		3	10	17	24	31
W		4	11	18	25	
T		5	12	19	26	
F		6	13	20	27	
S		7	14	21	28	
S	1	8	15	22	29	

Evie Hone was partially disabled due to infant paralysis and she required prolonged medical treatment, including visits to the continent. A visit to Assisi in 1911 made a deep religious impression on her, and her spirituality developed profoundly throughout her life. She studied under Sickert and Meninsky in London, and in 1920 she went to Paris with her friend Mainie Jellett where they became pupils of André Lhôte, and later of the Cubist painter Albert Gleizes. Hone and Jellett became pioneers of the new 'modern' painting movement in Ireland. Hone opened a studio in Rathfarnham in 1943. Ardmore's monastic ruins held a particular fascination for Hone, her enthusiasm for the place evidenced in this oil by the strong colours of the sky, hills and churchyard, and in the dynamic, rhythmic diagonal lines of the composition.

APRIL 2005

Week 15

April 2005					
M		4	11	18	25
T		5	12	19	26
W		6	13	20	27
T		7	14	21	28
F	1	8	15	22	29
S	2	9	16	23	30
S	3	10	17	24	

MONDAY 4

TUESDAY 5

WEDNESDAY 6

THURSDAY 7

FRIDAY 8

SATURDAY 9 / SUNDAY 10

May 2005

M		2	9	16	23	30
T		3	10	17	24	31
W		4	11	18	25	
T		5	12	19	26	
F		6	13	20	27	
S		7	14	21	28	
S	1	8	15	22	29	

APRIL 2005

Week 16

MONDAY 11

TUESDAY 12

WEDNESDAY 13

THURSDAY 14

FRIDAY 15

SATURDAY 16 / SUNDAY 17

Mill near Beggar's Bush, Co. Dublin

c. 1813

Francis Danby *(1793–1861)*

Watercolour on paper
21 x 27.9 cm

Francis Danby left Ireland permanently in 1813, settling in Bristol. This is one of four small watercolours which represent his early Irish work, which is very rare. Ringsend and Beggar's Bush are now suburbs of Dublin, south of where the River Liffey enters Dublin Bay and where it is joined by the River Dodder. According to a local historian, Mr Danny Parkinson of Donnybrook, the site of this charming rustic flour mill can be found opposite the present entrance to Lansdowne Road rugby ground.

March 2005

M		7	14	21	28
T	1	8	15	22	29
W	2	9	16	23	30
T	3	10	17	24	31
F	4	11	18	25	
S	5	12	19	26	
S	6	13	20	27	

April 2005

M		4	11	18	25
T		5	12	19	26
W		6	13	20	27
T		7	14	21	28
F	1	8	15	22	29
S	2	9	16	23	30
S	3	10	17	24	

May 2005

M		2	9	16	23	30
T		3	10	17	24	31
W		4	11	18	25	
T		5	12	19	26	
F		6	13	20	27	
S		7	14	21	28	
S	1	8	15	22	29	

Danby

APRIL 2005

April 2005

M		4	11	18	25
T		5	12	19	26
W		6	13	20	27
T		7	14	21	28
F	1	8	15	22	29
S	2	9	16	23	30
S	3	10	17	24	

Week 17

MONDAY 18

THURSDAY 21

TUESDAY 19

FRIDAY 22

WEDNESDAY 20

SATURDAY 23 / SUNDAY 24

May 2005

M		2	9	16	23	30
T		3	10	17	24	31
W		4	11	18	25	
T		5	12	19	26	
F		6	13	20	27	
S		7	14	21	28	
S	1	8	15	22	29	

APRIL / MAY 2005

Week 18

MONDAY 25

TUESDAY 26

WEDNESDAY 27

THURSDAY 28

FRIDAY 29

SATURDAY 30 / SUNDAY 1

Antrim Round Tower

1885

M Crawford *(19th century)*

Oil on canvas
68.5 x 45.6 cm

This is dated 1885, and was presented to the Museum by Miss Bessie Maconachie in 1977. The artist was presumably amateur. Known locally as "the steeple", Antrim round tower is the tallest remaining complete round tower in Ireland. These were monastic structures, constructed for defence and bell-ringing. Their doors are a considerable height above the ground, so that ladders could be pulled up inside for security in time of raid. They are quite unique to Ireland. The round tower is now surrounded by a public park called "The Steeple".

April 2005

M		4	11	18	25
T		5	12	19	26
W		6	13	20	27
T		7	14	21	28
F	1	8	15	22	29
S	2	9	16	23	30
S	3	10	17	24	

May 2005

M		2	9	16	23	30
T		3	10	17	24	31
W		4	11	18	25	
T		5	12	19	26	
F		6	13	20	27	
S		7	14	21	28	
S	1	8	15	22	29	

June 2005

M		6	13	20	27
T		7	14	21	28
W	1	8	15	22	29
T	2	9	16	23	30
F	3	10	17	24	
S	4	11	18	25	
S	5	12	19	26	

MAY 2005

May 2005

M		2	9	16	23	30
T		3	10	17	24	31
W		4	11	18	25	
T		5	12	19	26	
F		6	13	20	27	
S		7	14	21	28	
S	1	8	15	22	29	

Week 19

MONDAY 2

TUESDAY 3

WEDNESDAY 4

THURSDAY 5

FRIDAY 6

SATURDAY 7 / SUNDAY 8

June 2005

M		6	13	20	27
T		7	14	21	28
W	1	8	15	22	29
T	2	9	16	23	30
F	3	10	17	24	
S	4	11	18	25	
S	5	12	19	26	

MAY 2005

Week 20

MONDAY 9

TUESDAY 10

WEDNESDAY 11

THURSDAY 12

FRIDAY 13

SATURDAY 14 / SUNDAY 15

The Spanish Walk

Date unknown

Edwin A Morrow *(1877–1952)*

Oil on panel
16 x 21.6 cm

April 2005

M		4	11	18	25
T		5	12	19	26
W		6	13	20	27
T		7	14	21	28
F	1	8	15	22	29
S	2	9	16	23	30
S	3	10	17	24	

May 2005

M		2	9	16	23	30
T		3	10	17	24	31
W		4	11	18	25	
T		5	12	19	26	
F		6	13	20	27	
S		7	14	21	28	
S	1	8	15	22	29	

June 2005

M		6	13	20	27
T		7	14	21	28
W	1	8	15	22	29
T	2	9	16	23	30
F	3	10	17	24	
S	4	11	18	25	
S	5	12	19	26	

Edwin Morrow was one of eight sons of John Morrow, a Belfast painter and decorator. Edwin and four of his brothers studied art and became painters or illustrators: Albert (1863–1927), George (1869–1955), Jack (1872–1926), Edwin himself, and finally Norman, who died young. George Morrow, the best-known, became art editor of *Punch* in 1932. This oil by Edwin is one of a group of small West of Ireland scenes on panel, which belonged to the Belfast actor Michael Duffy, two of which were bought from him by the Ulster Museum in 1972. The long run of dwellings of the well-known Spanish Walk strings along the quayside of Galway City.

MAY 2005

May 2005

M		2	9	16	23	30
T		3	10	17	24	31
W		4	11	18	25	
T		5	12	19	26	
F		6	13	20	27	
S		7	14	21	28	
S	1	8	15	22	29	

Week 21

MONDAY 16

TUESDAY 17

WEDNESDAY 18

THURSDAY 19

FRIDAY 20

SATURDAY 21 / SUNDAY 22

June 2005

M		6	13	20	27
T		7	14	21	28
W	1	8	15	22	29
T	2	9	16	23	30
F	3	10	17	24	
S	4	11	18	25	
S	5	12	19	26	

MAY 2005

Week 22

MONDAY 23

TUESDAY 24

WEDNESDAY 25

THURSDAY 26

FRIDAY 27

SATURDAY 28 / SUNDAY 29

Haymaking at Maghera, Co. Donegal

Date unknown

Hugh Largey *(d.1992)*

Armagh County Museum
Oil on canvas
30.5 x 40.6 cm

Hugh Largey was a teacher at St Patrick's College, Armagh. This is a pleasant competent painting of a rural farming scene in the wilds of Donegal in a style recalling the County Antrim artist Charlie McAuley. The simple vernacular cottage at the centre of the painting, with its thatched roof and surrounded by the gathered hay, hardly intrudes on the natural landscape but rather appears to merge with it.

April 2005

M		4	11	18	25
T		5	12	19	26
W		6	13	20	27
T		7	14	21	28
F	1	8	15	22	29
S	2	9	16	23	30
S	3	10	17	24	

May 2005

M		2	9	16	23	30
T		3	10	17	24	31
W		4	11	18	25	
T		5	12	19	26	
F		6	13	20	27	
S		7	14	21	28	
S	1	8	15	22	29	

June 2005

M		6	13	20	27
T		7	14	21	28
W	1	8	15	22	29
T	2	9	16	23	30
F	3	10	17	24	
S	4	11	18	25	
S	5	12	19	26	

MAY / JUNE 2005

May 2005

M		2	9	16	23	30
T		3	10	17	24	31
W		4	11	18	25	
T		5	12	19	26	
F		6	13	20	27	
S		7	14	21	28	
S	1	8	15	22	29	

Week 23

MONDAY 30

THURSDAY 2

TUESDAY 31

FRIDAY 3

WEDNESDAY 1

SATURDAY 4 / SUNDAY 5

June 2005

M		6	13	20	27
T		7	14	21	28
W	1	8	15	22	29
T	2	9	16	23	30
F	3	10	17	24	
S	4	11	18	25	
S	5	12	19	26	

JUNE 2005

Week 24

MONDAY 6

TUESDAY 7

WEDNESDAY 8

THURSDAY 9

FRIDAY 10

SATURDAY 11 / SUNDAY 12

Ecclesiastical Ruins at Inniscaltra, or Holy Island, Lough Derg, Co. Galway

c. 1863

Bartholomew Colles Watkins *(1833–1891)*

Oil on canvas
104.3 x 153 cm

A regular exhibitor at the Royal Hibernian Academy from 1860, Colles Watkins devoted himself to painting Irish landscape in a particularly detailed style. Places like Connemara and Killarney featured among his favourite sites. As he worked slowly, his pictures are not plentiful. This is a very good example showing ancient Irish monastic ruins in the west of Ireland set against an evocative sunset. The round tower beside the church ruin is, of course, a distinctive Irish building type – other notable examples can be found at Glendalough, Antrim, Cashel and Kildare. On one of his sketching tours in Co. Kerry, Watkins caught a chill which turned to pneumonia, from which he died.

May 2005

M		2	9	16	23	30
T		3	10	17	24	31
W		4	11	18	25	
T		5	12	19	26	
F		6	13	20	27	
S		7	14	21	28	
S	1	8	15	22	29	

June 2005

M		6	13	20	27
T		7	14	21	28
W	1	8	15	22	29
T	2	9	16	23	30
F	3	10	17	24	
S	4	11	18	25	
S	5	12	19	26	

July 2005

M		4	11	18	25
T		5	12	19	26
W		6	13	20	27
T		7	14	21	28
F	1	8	15	22	29
S	2	9	16	23	30
S	3	10	17	24	31

JUNE 2005

June 2005

M		6	13	20	27
T		7	14	21	28
W	1	8	15	22	29
T	2	9	16	23	30
F	3	10	17	24	
S	4	11	18	25	
S	5	12	19	26	

Week 25

MONDAY 13

TUESDAY 14

WEDNESDAY 15

THURSDAY 16

FRIDAY 17

SATURDAY 18 / SUNDAY 19

July 2005

M		4	11	18	25
T		5	12	19	26
W		6	13	20	27
T		7	14	21	28
F	1	8	15	22	29
S	2	9	16	23	30
S	3	10	17	24	31

JUNE 2005

Week 26

MONDAY 20

TUESDAY 21

WEDNESDAY 22

THURSDAY 23

FRIDAY 24

SATURDAY 25 / SUNDAY 26

Town and Castle of Carrickfergus

1886

William Hodson *(active in Belfast 1885–1889)*

Pencil, watercolour, white on paper
32.7 x 43 cm

May 2005

M		2	9	16	23	30
T		3	10	17	24	31
W		4	11	18	25	
T		5	12	19	26	
F		6	13	20	27	
S		7	14	21	28	
S	1	8	15	22	29	

June 2005

M		6	13	20	27
T		7	14	21	28
W	1	8	15	22	29
T	2	9	16	23	30
F	3	10	17	24	
S	4	11	18	25	
S	5	12	19	26	

July 2005

M		4	11	18	25
T		5	12	19	26
W		6	13	20	27
T		7	14	21	28
F	1	8	15	22	29
S	2	9	16	23	30
S	3	10	17	24	31

The Norman keep of Carrickfergus Castle is one of the most notable sights of Ireland, and this attractive nineteenth-century watercolour sets it off against the background hills which sweep down to Belfast Lough. The distinctive spire of St Nicholas's Parish Church – another notable historic building – can be seen rising above the town on the right of the picture. An active member of the Belfast Ramblers' Sketching Club (the ancestor of the Royal Ulster Academy), Hodson served as treasurer and secretary. James Stelfox, who donated this painting to the Belfast Museum, was a distinguished naturalist, who worked for many years in the Natural History Division of the National Museum of Ireland, Dublin. His wife was one of the first women members of the Ramblers' Sketching Club, running the ladies' life classes which met once a week. The style of the watercolour suggests that Hodson may have been a pupil of James Howard Burgess.

JUNE / JULY 2005

June 2005

M		6	13	20	27
T		7	14	21	28
W	1	8	15	22	29
T	2	9	16	23	30
F	3	10	17	24	
S	4	11	18	25	
S	5	12	19	26	

Week 27

MONDAY 27

TUESDAY 28

WEDNESDAY 29

THURSDAY 30

FRIDAY 1

SATURDAY 2 / SUNDAY 3

July 2005

M		4	11	18	25
T		5	12	19	26
W		6	13	20	27
T		7	14	21	28
F	1	8	15	22	29
S	2	9	16	23	30
S	3	10	17	24	31

JULY 2005

Week 28

MONDAY 4

TUESDAY 5

WEDNESDAY 6

THURSDAY 7

FRIDAY 8

SATURDAY 9 / SUNDAY 10

Parish Church of Knock-Breda at the Newtown-Breda, Co. Down

1860

Rose Carruthers *(19th century)*

Watercolour on paper
17.4 x 30.4 cm

This charming primitive painting, dated 1861, was donated to the Museum by T Edens Osborne in 1921. The elegant little parish church of Newtownbreda or Knockbreda, designed by Richard Cassels of Dublin in the early 18th century for the Bateson family of Belvoir, still stands much as it appears here, though the surroundings are built over. Andrew Nicholl painted this church many times, and his amateur pupil Dr James Moore is buried in the churchyard, which commands an extensive view over Belfast and the surrounding countryside.

June 2005

M		6	13	20	27
T		7	14	21	28
W	1	8	15	22	29
T	2	9	16	23	30
F	3	10	17	24	
S	4	11	18	25	
S	5	12	19	26	

July 2005

M		4	11	18	25
T		5	12	19	26
W		6	13	20	27
T		7	14	21	28
F	1	8	15	22	29
S	2	9	16	23	30
S	3	10	17	24	31

August 2005

M	1	8	15	22	29
T	2	9	16	23	30
W	3	10	17	24	31
T	4	11	18	25	
F	5	12	19	26	
S	6	13	20	27	
S	7	14	21	28	

Rose Carruthers

JULY 2005

July 2005

M		4	11	18	25
T		5	12	19	26
W		6	13	20	27
T		7	14	21	28
F	1	8	15	22	29
S	2	9	16	23	30
S	3	10	17	24	31

Week 29

MONDAY 11

THURSDAY 14

TUESDAY 12

FRIDAY 15

WEDNESDAY 13

SATURDAY 16 / SUNDAY 17

August 2005

M	1	8	15	22	29
T	2	9	16	23	30
W	3	10	17	24	31
T	4	11	18	25	
F	5	12	19	26	
S	6	13	20	27	
S	7	14	21	28	

JULY 2005

Week 30

MONDAY 18

TUESDAY 19

WEDNESDAY 20

THURSDAY 21

FRIDAY 22

SATURDAY 23 / SUNDAY 24

Old Houses, Howth

1887

Joseph William Carey *(1859–1937)*

Pencil, watercolour, white on paper
25 x 35 cm

June 2005

M		6	13	20	27
T		7	14	21	28
W	1	8	15	22	29
T	2	9	16	23	30
F	3	10	17	24	
S	4	11	18	25	
S	5	12	19	26	

July 2005

M		4	11	18	25
T		5	12	19	26
W		6	13	20	27
T		7	14	21	28
F	1	8	15	22	29
S	2	9	16	23	30
S	3	10	17	24	31

August 2005

M	1	8	15	22	29
T	2	9	16	23	30
W	3	10	17	24	31
T	4	11	18	25	
F	5	12	19	26	
S	6	13	20	27	
S	7	14	21	28	

The elder brother of John Carey, J W Carey was one of the best watercolourists working in Belfast around the turn of the century. Like his brother, he worked at Marcus Ward's colour-printing factory for seven years, under John Vinycomb. In 1879 Carey had been one of the founder members of the Belfast Ramblers' Sketching Club, and in 1935 he was the oldest member of the Club's succeeding body, the Ulster Academy of Arts. Carey was interested in ballooning, sailing-boats and chess. He had two styles in watercolour, an early tightly-painted manner and a later, looser, more transparent style. This pleasing rural scene of the thatched and tumble-down cottages shows a corner of Howth, now a suburb north of Dublin, as it was in the late nineteenth century.

OLD HOUSES HOWTH
J.W. Carey 1887.

JULY 2005

July 2005

M		4	11	18	25
T		5	12	19	26
W		6	13	20	27
T		7	14	21	28
F	1	8	15	22	29
S	2	9	16	23	30
S	3	10	17	24	31

Week 31

MONDAY 25

THURSDAY 28

TUESDAY 26

FRIDAY 29

WEDNESDAY 27

SATURDAY 30 / SUNDAY 31

August 2005

M	1	8	15	22	29
T	2	9	16	23	30
W	3	10	17	24	31
T	4	11	18	25	
F	5	12	19	26	
S	6	13	20	27	
S	7	14	21	28	

AUGUST 2005

Week 32

MONDAY 1

TUESDAY 2

WEDNESDAY 3

THURSDAY 4

FRIDAY 5

SATURDAY 6 / SUNDAY 7

Lavery's at the Back of the Wood, Soldierstown

1903

Hugh Grant *(b. c.1865/67-d. c. 1947)*

Pastel on card
40.7 x 32 cm

July 2005

M		4	11	18	25
T		5	12	19	26
W		6	13	20	27
T		7	14	21	28
F	1	8	15	22	29
S	2	9	16	23	30
S	3	10	17	24	31

August 2005

M	1	8	15	22	29
T	2	9	16	23	30
W	3	10	17	24	31
T	4	11	18	25	
F	5	12	19	26	
S	6	13	20	27	
S	7	14	21	28	

September 2005

M		5	12	19	26
T		6	13	20	27
W		7	14	21	28
T	1	8	15	22	29
F	2	9	16	23	30
S	3	10	17	24	
S	4	11	18	25	

Grant is not mentioned in any textbooks, and little is known about him. He was deaf and dumb, and worked as a graphic artist for David Allen & Son, Belfast. He was married and had one son and one daughter; the son emigrated to the United States. Grant is buried in the New Cemetery at Larne. A well-proportioned three-bay late Georgian farmhouse is seen across a cornfield between trees, in bright sunshine. This is the farm between Soldierstown and Moira, Co. Down, where the orphaned John Lavery was brought up from the age of three by his uncle, Edward Lavery, at the end of the 1850s. It was then known as "the Back of the Wood", but was later called "Train View, Moira".

H GRANT

AUGUST 2005

August 2005					
M	1	8	15	22	29
T	2	9	16	23	30
W	3	10	17	24	31
T	4	11	18	25	
F	5	12	19	26	
S	6	13	20	27	
S	7	14	21	28	

Week 33

MONDAY 8

THURSDAY 11

TUESDAY 9

FRIDAY 12

WEDNESDAY 10

SATURDAY 13 / SUNDAY 14

September 2005

M		5	12	19	26
T		6	13	20	27
W		7	14	21	28
T	1	8	15	22	29
F	2	9	16	23	30
S	3	10	17	24	
S	4	11	18	25	

AUGUST 2005

Week 34

MONDAY 15

TUESDAY 16

WEDNESDAY 17

THURSDAY 18

FRIDAY 19

SATURDAY 20 / SUNDAY 21

Down Hill, the Seat of the Earl of Bristol

Date unknown

John Nixon *(c. 1750–1818)*

Watercolour on paper
14.5 x 22 cm

July 2005

M		4	11	18	25
T		5	12	19	26
W		6	13	20	27
T		7	14	21	28
F	1	8	15	22	29
S	2	9	16	23	30
S	3	10	17	24	31

August 2005

M	1	8	15	22	29
T	2	9	16	23	30
W	3	10	17	24	31
T	4	11	18	25	
F	5	12	19	26	
S	6	13	20	27	
S	7	14	21	28	

September 2005

M		5	12	19	26
T		6	13	20	27
W		7	14	21	28
T	1	8	15	22	29
F	2	9	16	23	30
S	3	10	17	24	
S	4	11	18	25	

The extremely wealthy Earl of Bristol, also a Church of Ireland bishop, built himself the splendid palace of Downhill in 1777, which now stands ruinous against the sky on the County Derry coastline. The mausoleum, seen here on the left of the picture, still stands intact, however, as does the famous Mussenden Temple perched precariously on the cliff-top, although the temple is not present in this scene. Nixon was an amateur London-based landscape painter and caricaturist, but he exhibited frequently at the Royal Academy from 1784 to 1815. He engraved a number of views of the seats of nobility – as here – many of which were engraved for a series published by the engraver William Watts. Nixon also drew other Irish sites such as Blarney, Carrickfergus, Dunluce and Shane's Castles and the Cavehill. He died at Ryde on the Isle of Wight, having provided the drawings for Thomas *Pennant's Journey from London to the Isle of Wight* (1801).

AUGUST 2005

August 2005

M	1	8	15	22	29
T	2	9	16	23	30
W	3	10	17	24	31
T	4	11	18	25	
F	5	12	19	26	
S	6	13	20	27	
S	7	14	21	28	

Week 35

MONDAY 22

TUESDAY 23

WEDNESDAY 24

THURSDAY 25

FRIDAY 26

SATURDAY 27 / SUNDAY 28

AUGUST / SEPTEMBER 2005

September 2005

M		5	12	19	26
T		6	13	20	27
W		7	14	21	28
T	1	8	15	22	29
F	2	9	16	23	30
S	3	10	17	24	
S	4	11	18	25	

Week 36

MONDAY 29

TUESDAY 30

WEDNESDAY 31

THURSDAY 1

FRIDAY 2

SATURDAY 3 / SUNDAY 4

Claddagh Duff, Connemara

c. 1950-51

George Campbell *(1917–1979)*

Oil on board
51.3 x 61.1 cm

August 2005

M	1	8	15	22	29
T	2	9	16	23	30
W	3	10	17	24	31
T	4	11	18	25	
F	5	12	19	26	
S	6	13	20	27	
S	7	14	21	28	

September 2005

M		5	12	19	26
T		6	13	20	27
W		7	14	21	28
T	1	8	15	22	29
F	2	9	16	23	30
S	3	10	17	24	
S	4	11	18	25	

October 2005

M		3	10	17	24	31
T		4	11	18	25	
W		5	12	19	26	
T		6	13	20	27	
F		7	14	21	28	
S	1	8	15	22	29	
S	2	9	16	23	30	

George Campbell, son of the primitive painter Gretta Bowen, and younger brother of Arthur Campbell, attended Richview School, Dublin, before the family moved north to Belfast. He left commercial work to become a full-time painter, a craft at which he was practically self-taught. This painting was presented to the Ulster Museum by the Thomas Haverty Trust in 1957. Claddagh Duff is a village in the most westerly part of Connemara. The vernacular dwellings, the simple Gothic church and the undulating stone walls seem to emerge naturally from the rocky landscape. The artist wrote, 'I painted it because I liked the build-up of textures and shapes; it is difficult to say precisely but the whole thing is a nice unit.'

SEPTEMBER 2005

September 2005

M		5	12	19	26
T		6	13	20	27
W		7	14	21	28
T	1	8	15	22	29
F	2	9	16	23	30
S	3	10	17	24	
S	4	11	18	25	

Week 37

MONDAY 5

TUESDAY 6

WEDNESDAY 7

THURSDAY 8

FRIDAY 9

SATURDAY 10 / SUNDAY 11

October 2005

M		3	10	17	24	31
T		4	11	18	25	
W		5	12	19	26	
T		6	13	20	27	
F		7	14	21	28	
S	1	8	15	22	29	
S	2	9	16	23	30	

SEPTEMBER 2005

Week 38

MONDAY 12

THURSDAY 15

TUESDAY 13

FRIDAY 16

WEDNESDAY 14

SATURDAY 17 / SUNDAY 18

The Four Courts, Dublin

1940

Norah McGuinness *(1901–1980)*

Gouache on paper
44 x 59.5 cm

August 2005

M	1	8	15	22	29
T	2	9	16	23	30
W	3	10	17	24	31
T	4	11	18	25	
F	5	12	19	26	
S	6	13	20	27	
S	7	14	21	28	

September 2005

M		5	12	19	26
T		6	13	20	27
W		7	14	21	28
T	1	8	15	22	29
F	2	9	16	23	30
S	3	10	17	24	
S	4	11	18	25	

October 2005

M		3	10	17	24	31
T		4	11	18	25	
W		5	12	19	26	
T		6	13	20	27	
F		7	14	21	28	
S	1	8	15	22	29	
S	2	9	16	23	30	

After a short period in New York, where she gained experience in designing window-dressing for a Fifth Avenue store, Norah McGuinness returned to Ireland permanently in 1939, making window displays for the Brown Thomas department store in Dublin. Her work at this time, mainly landscape and townscape, imitated the work of the French *Fauves* of thirty years before. In 1944 she succeeded Mainie Jellett as President of the Irish Exhibition of Living Art. With Nano Reid, she represented Ireland at the Venice Biennale of 1950. This painting imbues Gandon's imposing Neo-Classical Four Courts building and its north Liffey quayside setting with rich colour.

SEPTEMBER 2005

September 2005

M		5	12	19	26
T		6	13	20	27
W		7	14	21	28
T	1	8	15	22	29
F	2	9	16	23	30
S	3	10	17	24	
S	4	11	18	25	

Week 39

MONDAY 19

THURSDAY 22

TUESDAY 20

FRIDAY 23

WEDNESDAY 21

SATURDAY 24 / SUNDAY 25

SEPTEMBER / OCTOBER 2005

October 2005

M		3	10	17	24	31
T		4	11	18	25	
W		5	12	19	26	
T		6	13	20	27	
F		7	14	21	28	
S	1	8	15	22	29	
S	2	9	16	23	30	

Week 40

MONDAY 26

TUESDAY 27

WEDNESDAY 28

THURSDAY 29

FRIDAY 30

SATURDAY 1 / SUNDAY 2

Glenoe Village, Co. Antrim

Date unknown

Gerard Dillon *(1916–1971)*

Oil on board

40.6 x 30.5 cm

September 2005

M		5	12	19	26
T		6	13	20	27
W		7	14	21	28
T	1	8	15	22	29
F	2	9	16	23	30
S	3	10	17	24	
S	4	11	18	25	

October 2005

M		3	10	17	24	31
T		4	11	18	25	
W		5	12	19	26	
T		6	13	20	27	
F		7	14	21	28	
S	1	8	15	22	29	
S	2	9	16	23	30	

November 2005

M		7	14	21	28
T	1	8	15	22	29
W	2	9	16	23	30
T	3	10	17	24	
F	4	11	18	25	
S	5	12	19	26	
S	6	13	20	27	

Glenoe is a picturesque and much-painted small village near Larne, Co. Antrim, just inland from Larne Lough. The small simple whitewashed houses are characteristic of the rural Ulster landscape. Straightforward landscape subjects are not usually associated with Gerard Dillon, but this is a charming exception. Dillon, born off the Falls Road in Belfast, was a house painter-decorator who began painting seriously around 1936 and became one of the most imaginative of the folk-inspired Irish painters of the twentieth century. He visited Italy in 1947 and Spain about 1952. From 1958 he figured in international exhibitions in America, Rome and London, and toured Denmark and the USA. He visited and painted in the West of Ireland frequently and went to live in Dublin in 1968, where he died three years later in the Adelaide Hospital. He was buried in Belfast.

G. Dillon

OCTOBER 2005

October 2005

M		3	10	17	24	31
T		4	11	18	25	
W		5	12	19	26	
T		6	13	20	27	
F		7	14	21	28	
S	1	8	15	22	29	
S	2	9	16	23	30	

Week 41

MONDAY 3

THURSDAY 6

TUESDAY 4

FRIDAY 7

WEDNESDAY 5

SATURDAY 8 / SUNDAY 9

OCTOBER 2005

November 2005

M		7	14	21	28
T	1	8	15	22	29
W	2	9	16	23	30
T	3	10	17	24	
F	4	11	18	25	
S	5	12	19	26	
S	6	13	20	27	

Week 42

MONDAY 10

TUESDAY 11

WEDNESDAY 12

THURSDAY 13

FRIDAY 14

SATURDAY 15 / SUNDAY 16

Presbyterian Meeting House, Glenarm

18th century

Pupil of John James Barralet *(b. c. 1747-1815)*

Watercolour on paper
29.8 x 48.8 cm

September 2005

M		5	12	19	26
T		6	13	20	27
W		7	14	21	28
T	1	8	15	22	29
F	2	9	16	23	30
S	3	10	17	24	
S	4	11	18	25	

October 2005

M		3	10	17	24	31
T		4	11	18	25	
W		5	12	19	26	
T		6	13	20	27	
F		7	14	21	28	
S	1	8	15	22	29	
S	2	9	16	23	30	

November 2005

M		7	14	21	28
T	1	8	15	22	29
W	2	9	16	23	30
T	3	10	17	24	
F	4	11	18	25	
S	5	12	19	26	
S	6	13	20	27	

This is one of eight very interesting drawings of Glenarm and its vicinity, which were bought in a paper folder inscribed "Views of - from - or near / Glenarm - in 1787-88-89 -/ Mostly by Mr Barrales [*sic*] / artist and drawing master". That they are not all by the same hand is confirmed by the fact that two of the dated drawings are dated 1796, a year after Barralet emigrated to Philadelphia. The series gives ample evidence that Barralet worked for the McDonnell family at Glenarm Castle during his perambulations as a drawing master.

OCTOBER 2005

October 2005

M		3	10	17	24	31
T		4	11	18	25	
W		5	12	19	26	
T		6	13	20	27	
F		7	14	21	28	
S	1	8	15	22	29	
S	2	9	16	23	30	

Week 43

MONDAY 17

TUESDAY 18

WEDNESDAY 19

THURSDAY 20

FRIDAY 21

SATURDAY 22 / SUNDAY 23

November 2005

M		7	14	21	28
T	1	8	15	22	29
W	2	9	16	23	30
T	3	10	17	24	
F	4	11	18	25	
S	5	12	19	26	
S	6	13	20	27	

OCTOBER 2005

Week 44

MONDAY 24

TUESDAY 25

WEDNESDAY 26

THURSDAY 27

FRIDAY 28

SATURDAY 29 / SUNDAY 30

College Street, Armagh

1920

Clara Irwin *(1853-1921)*

Armagh County Museum
Watercolour on paper
14.5 x 14.3 cm

September 2005

M		5	12	19	26
T		6	13	20	27
W		7	14	21	28
T	1	8	15	22	29
F	2	9	16	23	30
S	3	10	17	24	
S	4	11	18	25	

October 2005

M		3	10	17	24	31
T		4	11	18	25	
W		5	12	19	26	
T		6	13	20	27	
F		7	14	21	28	
S	1	8	15	22	29	
S	2	9	16	23	30	

November 2005

M		7	14	21	28
T	1	8	15	22	29
W	2	9	16	23	30
T	3	10	17	24	
F	4	11	18	25	
S	5	12	19	26	
S	6	13	20	27	

Painted in 1920, this watercolour was donated to Armagh Museum by Mrs Houston in 1959. It joined a group of four similar views of Armagh streets by the same artist, donated by the Friends of Armagh County Museum in 1953. The view is taken from the western end of the Mall, with the classical portico of Francis Johnston's Court House on the right, and St Patrick's Church of Ireland Cathedral on the hill, dominating the little city.

OCTOBER / NOVEMBER 2005

October 2005

M		3	10	17	24	31
T		4	11	18	25	
W		5	12	19	26	
T		6	13	20	27	
F		7	14	21	28	
S	1	8	15	22	29	
S	2	9	16	23	30	

Week 45

MONDAY 31

TUESDAY 1

WEDNESDAY 2

THURSDAY 3

FRIDAY 4

SATURDAY 5 / SUNDAY 6

November 2005

M		7	14	21	28
T	1	8	15	22	29
W	2	9	16	23	30
T	3	10	17	24	
F	4	11	18	25	
S	5	12	19	26	
S	6	13	20	27	

NOVEMBER 2005

Week 46

MONDAY 7

THURSDAY 10

TUESDAY 8

FRIDAY 11

WEDNESDAY 9

SATURDAY 12 / SUNDAY 13

Cahan Abbey, with the O'Cahan Tomb, Dungiven, Co. Londonderry

19th century

James Howard Burgess *(c. 1810–1890)*

Pencil, watercolour, white on paper
35.5 x 26.3 cm

This attractive and detailed sketch reveals the romantic Victorian fascination with ecclesiastical ruins, with nature taking over the ancient Gothic arches. The O'Cahan family was closely associated with the Augustinian foundation of St Mary's Priory, Dungiven, and one of its family members lies beneath the elaborate traceried arch seen here. James Howard Burgess was an accomplished painter of landscapes and miniatures and practised in Belfast, Dublin and around Carrickfergus, also finding time to paint in Scotland and England. Many of his illustrations were included in Hall's *Ireland, Its Scenery, Character (1841) and Illustrations of the North of Ireland published by Marcus Ward; his Sketches from Nature in Ireland* appeared in Friedel's *Drawing Book* published in London. Burgess died in Belfast. His work is found in the Ulster Museum, the Armagh County Museum and the National Gallery of Ireland, and many of his lithographs are housed at the Linen Hall Library, Belfast and at the National Library of Ireland in Dublin.

October 2005

M		3	10	17	24	31
T		4	11	18	25	
W		5	12	19	26	
T		6	13	20	27	
F		7	14	21	28	
S	1	8	15	22	29	
S	2	9	16	23	30	

November 2005

M		7	14	21	28
T	1	8	15	22	29
W	2	9	16	23	30
T	3	10	17	24	
F	4	11	18	25	
S	5	12	19	26	
S	6	13	20	27	

December 2005

M		5	12	19	26
T		6	13	20	27
W		7	14	21	28
T	1	8	15	22	29
F	2	9	16	23	30
S	3	10	17	24	31
S	4	11	18	25	

NOVEMBER 2005

November 2005

M		7	14	21	28
T	1	8	15	22	29
W	2	9	16	23	30
T	3	10	17	24	
F	4	11	18	25	
S	5	12	19	26	
S	6	13	20	27	

Week 47

MONDAY 14

THURSDAY 17

TUESDAY 15

FRIDAY 18

WEDNESDAY 16

SATURDAY 19 / SUNDAY 20

NOVEMBER 2005

December 2005

M		5	12	19	26
T		6	13	20	27
W		7	14	21	28
T	1	8	15	22	29
F	2	9	16	23	30
S	3	10	17	24	31
S	4	11	18	25	

Week 48

MONDAY 21

TUESDAY 22

WEDNESDAY 23

THURSDAY 24

FRIDAY 25

SATURDAY 26 / SUNDAY 27

Ormond Quay, Dublin

c. 1939

Tom Carr *(1909–1999)*

Watercolour on paper

21.6 x 27.4 cm (sight)

October 2005

M		3	10	17	24	31
T		4	11	18	25	
W		5	12	19	26	
T		6	13	20	27	
F		7	14	21	28	
S	1	8	15	22	29	
S	2	9	16	23	30	

November 2005

M		7	14	21	28
T	1	8	15	22	29
W	2	9	16	23	30
T	3	10	17	24	
F	4	11	18	25	
S	5	12	19	26	
S	6	13	20	27	

December 2005

M		5	12	19	26
T		6	13	20	27
W		7	14	21	28
T	1	8	15	22	29
F	2	9	16	23	30
S	3	10	17	24	31
S	4	11	18	25	

During February and March 1939 Tom Carr visited Dublin with the South African painter Graham Bell (1910–43), a fellow pupil at the Realist Euston Road school in London. They had already painted together at Dover in 1938. They made a contract to hold an exhibition in Dublin after painting pictures in the city. Bell at this time was deeply involved in anti-fascist propaganda, but the Dublin episode enabled him for a short time to concentrate on objective painting. Carr was a less analytical painter than the orthodox Euston Roaders, and less dogmatic than the Objective Abstractionists to whom he had previously been attached. This painting depicts the colourfully painted string of Georgian buildings that run along the north quayside of the River Liffey between O'Connell Street and the Four Courts.

NOVEMBER / DECEMBER 2005

November 2005

M		7	14	21	28
T	1	8	15	22	29
W	2	9	16	23	30
T	3	10	17	24	
F	4	11	18	25	
S	5	12	19	26	
S	6	13	20	27	

Week 49

MONDAY 28

THURSDAY 1

TUESDAY 29

FRIDAY 2

WEDNESDAY 30

SATURDAY 3 / SUNDAY 4

December 2005

M		5	12	19	26
T		6	13	20	27
W		7	14	21	28
T	1	8	15	22	29
F	2	9	16	23	30
S	3	10	17	24	31
S	4	11	18	25	

DECEMBER 2005

Week 50

MONDAY 5

THURSDAY 8

TUESDAY 6

FRIDAY 9

WEDNESDAY 7

SATURDAY 10 / SUNDAY 11

A View of Kilkenny

c. 1800

Edmund Garvey *(d. 1808)*

Oil on canvas
91.4 x 152.3 cm

November 2005

M		7	14	21	28
T	1	8	15	22	29
W	2	9	16	23	30
T	3	10	17	24	
F	4	11	18	25	
S	5	12	19	26	
S	6	13	20	27	

December 2005

M		5	12	19	26
T		6	13	20	27
W		7	14	21	28
T	1	8	15	22	29
F	2	9	16	23	30
S	3	10	17	24	31
S	4	11	18	25	

January 2006

M		2	9	16	23	30
T		3	10	17	24	31
W		4	11	18	25	
T		5	12	19	26	
F		6	13	20	27	
S		7	14	21	28	
S	1	8	15	22	29	

This painting of Edmund Garvey's native city was bought in 1971 as by Nathaniel Grogan, but re-attributed to Garvey by Anne Crookshank and the Knight of Glin. The view is taken from Windy Gap, on the outskirts of Kilkenny. A city of much architectural distinction, on the left is Kilkenny Castle, seat of the Dukes of Ormond, standing above the River Nore, and on the right St Canice's Cathedral with its round tower can be seen. Much of Garvey's career was spent in England where he painted views of country houses for the gentry. He exhibited his Irish views at the Royal Academy between 1784 and 1802.

DECEMBER 2005

December 2005					
M		5	12	19	26
T		6	13	20	27
W		7	14	21	28
T	1	8	15	22	29
F	2	9	16	23	30
S	3	10	17	24	31
S	4	11	18	25	

Week 51

MONDAY 12

TUESDAY 13

WEDNESDAY 14

THURSDAY 15

FRIDAY 16

SATURDAY 17 / SUNDAY 18

January 2006

M		2	9	16	23	30
T		3	10	17	24	31
W		4	11	18	25	
T		5	12	19	26	
F		6	13	20	27	
S		7	14	21	28	
S	1	8	15	22	29	

DECEMBER 2005

Week 52

MONDAY 19

THURSDAY 22

TUESDAY 20

FRIDAY 23

WEDNESDAY 21

SATURDAY 24 / SUNDAY 25

The Island Cross, Tynan

Date unknown

Lady Daphne Pitt-Taylor *(1889-1945)*

Armagh County Museum
Watercolour on paper
30.4 x 22.2 cm

This cross, eight feet six inches high with solid ring, raised and incised lines and traces of a central figure, was removed from Glenarb in the mid 19th century to its present site in the demesne of Tynan Abbey, eight miles south of Armagh. Two other crosses were brought to the demesne by Sir James Stronge, 5th Baronet, from other parts of his property. The stone cross in the village of Tynan is in state care. The artist was Sir James Stronge's daughter, who studied in London, Switzerland, France and Italy. In 1920 she married General Sir Walter Pitt-Taylor, who for a time was stationed in India. Some of her work was destroyed in a fire at Tynan Abbey in 1981.

November 2005

M		7	14	21	28
T	1	8	15	22	29
W	2	9	16	23	30
T	3	10	17	24	
F	4	11	18	25	
S	5	12	19	26	
S	6	13	20	27	

December 2005

M		5	12	19	26
T		6	13	20	27
W		7	14	21	28
T	1	8	15	22	29
F	2	9	16	23	30
S	3	10	17	24	31
S	4	11	18	25	

January 2006

M		2	9	16	23	30
T		3	10	17	24	31
W		4	11	18	25	
T		5	12	19	26	
F		6	13	20	27	
S		7	14	21	28	
S	1	8	15	22	29	

DECEMBER 2005 / JANUARY 2006

December 2005

M		5	12	19	26
T		6	13	20	27
W		7	14	21	28
T	1	8	15	22	29
F	2	9	16	23	30
S	3	10	17	24	31
S	4	11	18	25	

Week 1

MONDAY 26

THURSDAY 29

TUESDAY 27

FRIDAY 30

WEDNESDAY 28

SATURDAY 31 / SUNDAY 1

January 2006

M		2	9	16	23	30
T		3	10	17	24	31
W		4	11	18	25	
T		5	12	19	26	
F		6	13	20	27	
S		7	14	21	28	
S	1	8	15	22	29	

JANUARY 2006

Week 2

MONDAY 2

THURSDAY 5

TUESDAY 3

FRIDAY 6

WEDNESDAY 4

SATURDAY 7 / SUNDAY 8

The City Hall under Snow

c. 1920s

William Conor *(1881–1968)*

Oil on canvas on board
42.9 x 53.3 cm

November 2005

M		7	14	21	28
T	1	8	15	22	29
W	2	9	16	23	30
T	3	10	17	24	
F	4	11	18	25	
S	5	12	19	26	
S	6	13	20	27	

December 2005

M		5	12	19	26
T		6	13	20	27
W		7	14	21	28
T	1	8	15	22	29
F	2	9	16	23	30
S	3	10	17	24	31
S	4	11	18	25	

January 2006

M		2	9	16	23	30
T		3	10	17	24	31
W		4	11	18	25	
T		5	12	19	26	
F		6	13	20	27	
S		7	14	21	28	
S	1	8	15	22	29	

This wintry view of Belfast's most famous Edwardian landmark – Sir Alfred Brumwell Thomas's grand Baroque Revival City Hall – was probably painted in the 1920s, at a time when Conor was establishing himself as the most popular and representative Belfast painter of his generation. Like many Belfast artists, he began his career as a lithographic technician or 'black man' with the local poster firm of David Allen. He was a brilliant recorder of Belfast scenery and life, and though held in high popular esteem, he lived modestly and was never financially successful. The City Hall, constructed of Portland stone and noted for its central copper dome, forms the centrepiece of the Belfast cityscape.

Conor

JANUARY 2006

January 2006						
M		2	9	16	23	30
T		3	10	17	24	31
W		4	11	18	25	
T		5	12	19	26	
F		6	13	20	27	
S		7	14	21	28	
S	1	8	15	22	29	

Week 3

MONDAY 9

TUESDAY 10

WEDNESDAY 11

THURSDAY 12

FRIDAY 13

SATURDAY 14 / SUNDAY 15

February 2006

M		6	13	20	27
T		7	14	21	28
W	1	8	15	22	
T	2	9	16	23	
F	3	10	17	24	
S	4	11	18	25	
S	5	12	19	26	

JANUARY 2006

Week 4

MONDAY 16

TUESDAY 17

WEDNESDAY 18

THURSDAY 19

FRIDAY 20

SATURDAY 21 / SUNDAY 22

List of Illustrations

week		
28	*Parish Church of Knock-Breda at the Newtown-Breda, Co. Down*	Rose Carruthers
30	*Old Houses, Howth*	Joseph William Carey
32	*Lavery's at the Back of the Wood, Soldierstown*	Hugh Grant
34	*Down Hill, the Seat of the Earl of Bristol*	John Nixon
36	*Claddagh Duff, Connemara*	George Campbell
38	*The Four Courts, Dublin*	Norah McGuinness
40	*Glenoe Village, Co. Antrim*	Gerard Dillon
42	*Presbyterian Meeting House, Glenarm*	Pupil of John James Barralet
44	*College Street, Armagh*	Clara Irwin
46	*Cahan Abbey with the O'Cahan Tomb, Dungiven, Co. Londonderry*	James Howard Burgess
48	*Ormond Quay, Dublin*	Tom Carr
50	*A View of Kilkenny*	Edmund Garvey
52	*The Island Cross, Tynan*	Lady Daphne Pitt-Taylor
1	*The City Hall under Snow*	William Conor

Acknowledgements

The publisher wishes to thank the following for permission to reproduce work in copyright:

The Ulster Museum; Mrs Margaret Campbell for *Claddagh Duff*, Connemara by George Campbell (© Mrs Margaret Campbell); Mr Alan Carey for *Old Houses, Howth* by Joseph William Carey (© Mr Alan Carey); Estate of Tom Carr for *Ormond Quay, Dublin* by Tom Carr (© Estate of Tom Carr); Estate of William Conor for *The City Hall under Snow* by William Conor (© Estate of William Conor); Gerard Dillon for *Glenoe Village, Co. Antrim* by Gerard Dillon (© Gerard Dillon); Miss Rhoda McGuinness for *The Four Courts, Dublin* by Norah McGuinness (© Miss Rhoda McGunness)

While every effort has been made to contact copyright holders, the publisher would welcome information on any oversight which may have occurred.

Text by Martyn Anglesea (Keeper of Fine Art, Ulster Museum)

The publisher wishes to thank Pat McLean, Rights and Reproductions Officer, Ulster Museum for her help in compiling this collection.